The Magic School Bus
Lost in the Solar System

By Joanna Cole   Illustrated by Bruce Degen

SCHOLASTIC
HARDCOVER

SCHOLASTIC INC. / *New York*

The author and illustrator wish to thank
Dr. Donna L. Gresh,
Center for Radar Astronomy at Stanford University,
for her assistance in preparing this book.

The author also thanks John Stoke,
Astronomical Writer/Producer at the American Museum-Hayden Planetarium,
for his helpful advice.

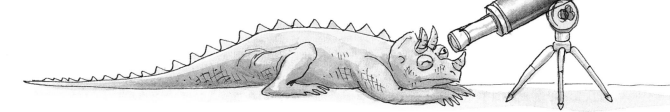

Library of Congress Cataloging-in-Publication Data
Cole, Joanna.
The magic school bus, lost in the solar system.
Summary: On a special field trip in the magic school bus,
Ms. Frizzle's class goes into outer space and visits each planet
in the solar system.
1. Outer space—Exploration—Juvenile literature. 2. Astron-
omy—Juvenile literature. [1. Planets. 2. Solar System.
3. Astronomy.]
I.Degen, Bruce, ill. II. Title.
QB500.22.064   1990   523.3   89-10185
ISBN 0-590-41428-3

Printed in the U.S.A.

To Virginia and Bob McBride—J.C.

For Chris, queen of the
Biscadorian Mother ship—B.D.

Arnold's cousin Janet was
visiting our class for the day.
"I know all of you
will be nice to our guest," said the Friz.

We tried to be nice to Janet.
We really did.
As we got on the school bus,
we told her that Ms. Frizzle
is the weirdest teacher in school.
But Janet wasn't interested.
She wanted to tell us about herself.

As usual, it took a while to get the old bus started.
But finally we were on our way.
As we were driving, Ms. Frizzle told us all about how the Earth spins like a top as it moves in its orbit.
It was just a short drive to the planetarium, but Ms. Frizzle talked fast.

WHAT MAKES NIGHT AND DAY?
by Phoebe

The spinning of the Earth makes night and day.

When one side of the Earth faces the Sun, it is daytime on that side. When that side turns away from the Sun, it is night.

THIS BUS IS A WRECK.

AT LEAST IT STARTED THIS TIME.

WE HAVE NEW SCHOOL BUSES AT OUR SCHOOL.

WHEN THE EARTH SPINS WE SAY IT ROTATES. THE EARTH MAKES ONE COMPLETE ROTATION—TURN—EVERY 24 HOURS.

When we got to the planetarium,
it was closed for repairs.
"Class, this means we'll
have to return to school,"
said the Friz.
We were so disappointed!

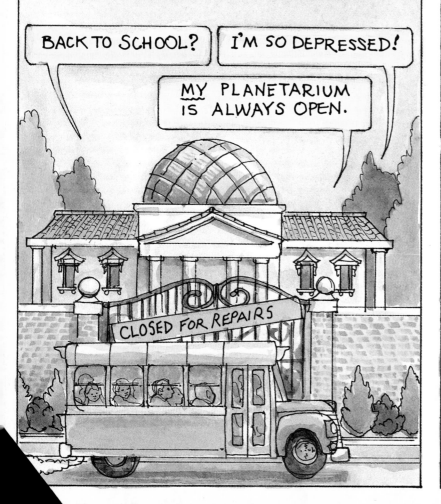

BACK TO SCHOOL?

I'M SO DEPRESSED!

MY PLANETARIUM
IS ALWAYS OPEN.

On the way back,
as we were waiting at a red light,
something amazing happened.
The bus started tilting back,
and we heard the roar of rockets.
"Oh, dear," said Ms. Frizzle.
"We seem to be blasting off!"

HERE WE
GO AGAIN.

NOT ANOTHE
CRAZY TRIP!

Far behind, in the black sky, we saw the planet Earth getting smaller and smaller. We were traveling in space! We had become astronauts!

The Friz said our first stop
would be the Moon.
We got off the bus and looked around.
There was no air, no water,
no sign of life.
All we saw were dust and rock
and lots and lots of craters.
Ms. Frizzle said the craters were
formed billions of years ago
when the Moon was hit by meteorites.
Meteorites are falling chunks
of rock and metal.

WE ARE SO LIGHT ON THE MOON!

THAT'S BECAUSE THE MOON HAS LESS GRAVITY THAN THE EARTH.

YOUR WEIGHT AND FATE ON THE MOON

lbs. 85 Earth weight

lbs. 14 Moon weight

You will travel to far off places.

It was fun on the Moon.
We wanted to play,
but Ms. Frizzle said it was time to go.
So we got back on the bus.
"We'll start with the Sun,
the center of the solar system,"
said the Friz, and we blasted off.

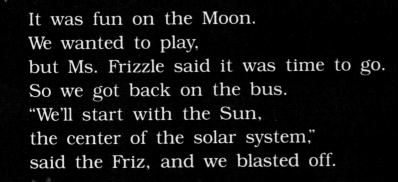

LOOK HOW HIGH WE CAN JUMP!

I WAS IN A NATIONAL JUMP-ROPE CONTEST. I WON, OF COURSE.

IS THERE A NATIONAL BRAGGING CONTEST?

WHAT MAKES THE MOON SHINE?
by Rachel
The Moon does not make any light of its own. The moonlight we see from Earth is really light from the sun. It hits the Moon and bounces off, the way light is reflected from a mirror.

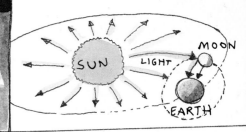

THE MOON'S ORBIT
by Amanda Jane
The Moon travels in orbit around the Earth, just as the Earth travels around the Sun.

THE SUN IS A STAR
by Carmen
Our Sun is an average star like the ones we see in the night sky.

WHICH STAR DO WE SEE ONLY IN THE DAYTIME?

THAT'S EASY: THE SUN.

HOW BIG IS THE SUN?
by Gregory
Our sun measures more than a million kilometers across. More than one million Earths could fit inside it!

We zoomed toward the Sun, the biggest, brightest, and hottest object in the solar system. Jets of super-hot gases shot out at us from the surface. Thank goodness Ms. Frizzle didn't get *too* close!

YOU SHOULD NEVER LOOK DIRECTLY AT THE SUN, CHILDREN. IT CAN DAMAGE YOUR EYES!

YOU SHOULD NEVER DRIVE A BUS DIRECTLY INTO THE SUN, EITHER!

HOT!

SOLAR FLARES are giant storms on the Sun's Surface.

"We'll be seeing all the planets in order, class," explained Frizzie. "Mercury is the first planet, the closest to the Sun."

MY SCHOOL IS HEATED WITH <u>SOLAR</u> ENERGY.

I HAVE A <u>SUN</u> DECK.

I HAVE TEN PAIRS OF <u>SUNGLASSES</u>.

GIVE US A BREAK, JANET.

SUN SPOTS are areas that are cooler than the rest of the Sun.

HOW HOT IS THE SUN?
by Florrie
At the center of the sun the temperature is about 15 <u>million</u> degrees Centigrade! The sun is so hot it heats planets that are millions of kilometers away.

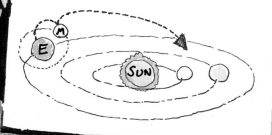

Our Path So Far

Mercury was a dead, sun-baked planet.
"This planet is a lot like our Moon.
There is no water and hardly any air,"
said the Friz.
"Notice the craters on its surface
as we pass by."

THE SUN LOOKS TWICE AS BIG HERE AS IT DOES FROM EARTH.

THAT'S BECAUSE MERCURY IS SO CLOSE.

TOO CLOSE! LET'S GO!

YOUR WEIGHT AND FATE ON MERCURY

lbs.
85
Earth Weight

lbs.
32
Mercury Weight

You Will Vacation in a Sunny Spot.

Before long, we felt ourselves
being pulled in by the gravity of Venus
—the second planet from the Sun.
Venus was completely covered by
a thick layer of yellowish clouds.
"We will now explore the surface of Venus,"
said Ms. Frizzle.

WHY ARE VENUS'S CLOUDS
YELLOW?
by Tim
Earth's clouds are
white because they are
made of water vapor.
Venus's clouds are
made mostly of a
deadly yellow poison
called _sulfuric acid_.

WE'RE GAINING
WEIGHT, AND WE
HAVEN'T EVEN
HAD LUNCH.

WE WILL BE HEAVIER
HERE THAN ON THE MOON
OR MERCURY BECAUSE
VENUS HAS MORE
GRAVITY.

YOUR WEIGHT AND FATE
ON VENUS

lbs.
85
Earth
Weight

lbs.
77
Venus
Weight

Your future
looks
Cloudy.

SO DOES VENUS!

WHY IS IT SO HOT ON VENUS?
by Ralph

Venus's atmosphere has a lot of carbon dioxide gas in it. Carbon dioxide acts like a blanket to hold heat in.

CLOUDS

HEAT HEAT HEAT

When heat is trapped like this by a planet's atmosphere, it is called the "greenhouse effect."

Below the clouds, Venus was as dry as a desert.
The ground was covered with rocks.
And it was HOT!
It was about 400 degrees Centigrade!
That's *much* hotter than an oven baking cookies!

THERE'S NO LIFE ON VENUS, CLASS.

IT'S TOO HOT!

IT'S TOO DRY!

THERE'S TOO MUCH ACID!

LET'S LEAVE.

The air was so heavy
we could feel it pressing down on us!
Ms. Frizzle said there might be volcanoes
around, too.
We said, "Let's get out of here!"
"Our next stop is Mars,
the red planet, fourth from the Sun,"
announced the Friz.
"On our way, we'll be passing through
the orbit of Earth, the third planet."
The bus lifted off with a roar.

I'VE BEEN TO MARS
LOTS OF TIMES.

JUST
IGNORE HER.

IT NEVER RAINS
ON VENUS
        by Dorothy Ann
Venus's clouds
never make rain
because it is too hot
for rain to form. Any
liquid on Venus dries
up instantly.

Our Path So Far

WHY AREN'T MARS'S MOONS ROUND?
by John

Large moons are round because of their gravity. Billions of years ago, when large moons formed, their gravity pulled in their material evenly and made them round.

The moons of Mars are so small that

they don't have enough gravity to be round.

As we came close to Mars,
we passed its two moons,
which are called Phobos and Deimos.
Compared to our Moon,
they were tiny.
And they weren't even round!

Phobos
(18 miles long)

Deimos
(9 miles long)

Volcano

LONG AGO, THERE MAY HAVE BEEN WATER IN THOSE CHANNELS.

YES, BUT TODAY ALL MARS'S WATER IS FROZEN IN THE POLAR ICE CAPS.

THOSE ARE MOONS?

THEY LOOK LIKE POTATOES WITH CRATERS.

Looking down, we saw a huge canyon.
Ms. Frizzle said it was
as long as the United States.
There was a volcano
three times taller than
the tallest volcano on Earth.
And all around, there were channels
that looked like dried-up river beds.

Polar Ice Cap

Canyon

Channels

EARTH IS THE
BEST PLANET FOR
LIFE. THAT'S WHY
I LIVE THERE.

JANET LIKES TO
BE THE BEST.

...TICED.

IS THERE LIFE ON MARS?
by Molly
No life has been
found on Mars.
Living things need
water, and there
is no liquid water
on Mars.
So space scientists
think life probably
cannot exist there!

YOUR WEIGHT AND FATE
ON MARS

lbs.	lbs.
85	32
Earth Weight	Mars Weight

Things will
look rosy
soon.

100

"Mars is the last of what we call
the inner planets!"
Ms. Frizzle shouted above the roar of the rockets.
"We will now be going
through the asteroid belt
to the outer planets!"

THE ASTEROID BELT
by Shirley
The area between the inner and the outer planets is called the asteroid belt. It is filled with thousands and thousands of asteroids.

WHAT ARE ASTEROIDS?
by Florrie
Asteroids are chunks of rock and metal in orbit around the Sun.
Scientists think they are the building blocks of a planet that never formed.

Thousands of asteroids were spinning all around us.
All at once, we heard the tinkling of broken glass.
One of our taillights had been hit by an asteroid.
Ms. Frizzle put the bus on autopilot and went out to take a look.
She kept on talking about asteroids over the bus radio.

THE LARGEST ASTEROID IS ONLY $\frac{1}{3}$ THE SIZE OF OUR MOON. MOST ASTEROIDS ARE THE SIZE OF HOUSES OR SMALLER.

I WISH SHE'D COME INSIDE.

Suddenly there was a snap.
Ms. Frizzle's tether line had broken!
Without warning,
the rockets fired up,
and the bus zoomed away!
The autopilot was malfunctioning.

On the radio, Ms. Frizzle's voice grew
fainter and fainter.
Then she was gone.
We were on our own!
We were lost in the solar system!

Most of us were too scared to move.
But Janet started searching the bus.
In the glove compartment
she found Ms. Frizzle's lesson book.
As she began reading from it,
a huge planet came into view.
"Class, this is Jupiter," Janet read.
"It's the first of the outer planets,
and the largest planet in the solar system."

"As we approach Jupiter, we can see some of its 16 moons."

"Arnold, are you listening?"

BOY, MS. FRIZZLE PLANS EVERYTHING!

SHE SHOULDN'T TOUCH MS. FRIZZLE'S THINGS.

BUT THIS IS AN EMERGENCY!

Lesson Plan
As we approach
Jupiter, we can
see some of its
16 moons.
"Arnold, are
you ?"

WHAT ARE SATURN'S RINGS?
by Rachel

Saturn's rings are made of ice, rock and dust — all in orbit around the planet.

The next sight made us forget our troubles.
It was Saturn, a gas planet like Jupiter.
It had swirling clouds and lots of moons.
But the most incredible thing about Saturn was its rings.
It was the most beautiful planet in the solar system!

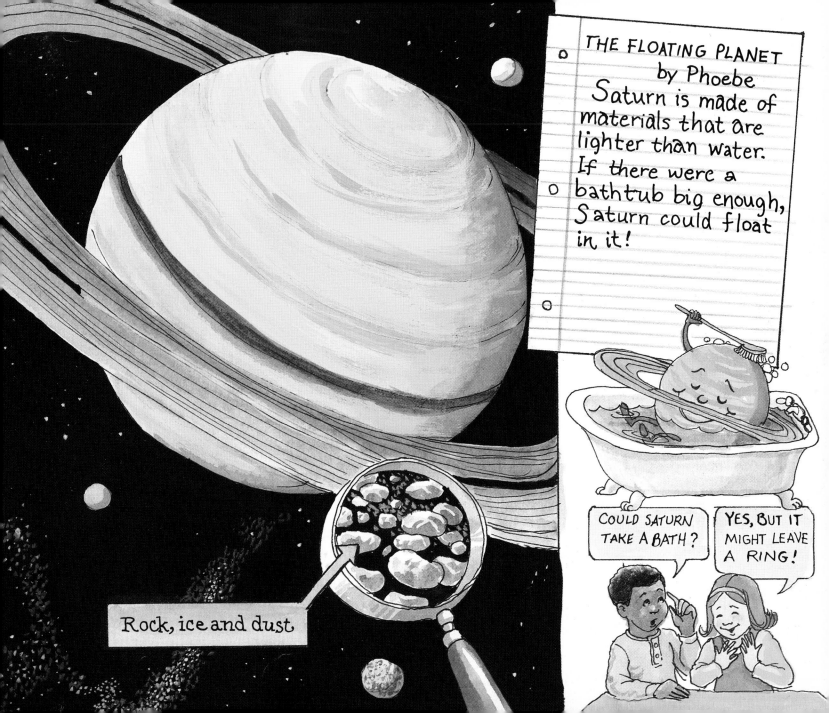

THE TIPPED OVER PLANET
by Ralph

Uranus spins differently from the other planets. It seems to be lying on its side compared to most other planets in the Solar System.

Uranus Earth Sun

YOUR WEIGHT AND FATE ON URANUS

lbs. 85 Earth Weight	lbs. 73 Uranus Weight

Feeling blue? You may be homesick.

Next was Uranus, a blue-green gas planet with faint gray rings and moons. Some scientists think they might be made of chunks of graphite— the material used in pencils on Earth.

"Methane gas in its atmosphere makes Uranus look blue."

YOU LOOK KIND OF BLUE YOURSELF.

I'M FREEZING!

THAT'S BECAUSE WE'RE SO FAR AWAY FROM THE SUN.

The bus was going faster and faster,
and we couldn't control the autopilot.
We swept past stormy Neptune,
another blue-green planet—eighth from the Sun.
All we could think about
was finding Ms. Frizzle!

"Neptune is the last of the giant gas planets."

WE'RE ALMOST OUT OF GAS OURSELVES!

Great Dark Spot

AND THE NEAREST SERVICE STATION IS 4,000 MILLION KILOMETERS AWAY.

o HOW LONG IS A YEAR?
by Tim
A year is the time it takes for a planet to go all around the sun. Neptune and
o Uranus are so far away from the sun that they have very long years.
o One year on Uranus is 84 Earth years.

Neptune's year is
o 165 Earth years.

YOUR WEIGHT AND FATE ON NEPTUNE

lbs. 85 Earth Weight

lbs. 97 Neptune Weight

You will have a happy birthday 165 years from now.

Janet flipped rapidly
through Ms. Frizzle's book.
Suddenly she found something new—
the instructions for the autopilot.
We punched in ASTEROID BELT
on the control panel.
Slowly the bus turned around.
It was working! We were going back!

ASTEROID BELT **

Auto-Pilot

JANET REALLY SAVED THE DAY.

I TOLD YOU SHE'S A GOOD KID.

- BEYOND PLUTO:
  STARS AND MORE STARS
        by Alex
  Beyond our solar
  system are _billions_ and
  billions of stars. There
- are so many stars and
  they are so far away
  that our minds cannot
  even imagine it.
  Some of those stars
- may have planets,
  and some of those

- planets could have
  life on them, just
  like our earth.

Our Path so far

Asteroid Belt

With Frizzie back at the wheel,
the bus headed straight for Earth.
We reentered the atmosphere,
landed with a thump,
and looked around.

BOYS AND GIRLS,
WE ARE ARRIVING
ON EARTH, THE
THIRD PLANET
FROM THE SUN.

THUMP

We were in the school parking lot again.
The rockets were gone.
The space suits were gone.
The bus was a wreck.
Everything was back to normal.

THANK GOODNESS!

HELLO AGAIN,
OLD FRIEND.

OUR PLANET CHART

PLANET	HOW BIG ACROSS	HOW LONG ONE ROTATION (DAY AND NIGHT)	HOW LONG ONE YEAR	HOW FAR FROM THE SUN	HOW MANY MOONS	HOW MANY RINGS
MERCURY	4,900 km.	59 days	88 days	57.9 million km.	None	None
VENUS	12,100 km.	243 days	224.7 days	108.2 million km.	None	None
EARTH	12,756 km.	24 hours	365.3 days	149.6 million Km.	1	None
MARS	6,800 Km.	24.5 hours	687 days	227.8 million Km.	2	None
JUPITER	142,800 Km.	9.8 hours	12 Earth Years	778 million Km.	at least 16	2
SATURN	120,660 km.	10.7 hours	29.5 Earth Years	1,427 million Km.	at least 17	Many
URANUS	52,400 km.	17 hours	84 Earth Years	2,870 million Km.	at least 15	10
NEPTUNE	49,500 Km.	16 hours	165 Earth Years	4,500 million Km.	8	4
PLUTO	about 2,300 km.	6 days	248 Earth Years	5,900 million Km.	1	None

In the classroom,
we made a terrific
chart of the planets
and a mobile of the solar system.

At last, it was time to go home.
It had been a typical day
in Ms. Frizzle's class.
Now we had only one problem.
Would anyone ever believe us
when we told about our trip?

OUR FISH FRIENDS

OCEANS & SEAS

ATTENTION, READERS!

<u>DO NOT</u> ATTEMPT THIS TRIP ON YOUR OWN SCHOOL BUS!

Three reasons why not:

1. Attaching rockets to your school bus will upset your teacher, the school principal, and your parents. It will not get you into orbit anyway. An ordinary bus cannot travel in outer space, and you cannot become astronauts without years of training.

2. Landing on certain planets may be dangerous to your health. Even astronauts cannot visit Venus (it's too hot), Mercury (it's too close to the Sun), or Jupiter (its gravity would crush human beings). People cannot fly to the Sun, either. Its gravity and heat would be too strong.

3. Space travel could make you miss dinner with your family... for the rest of your childhood. Even if a school bus <u>could</u> go to outer space, it could never travel through the entire solar system in one day. It took <u>years</u> for the Voyager space probes to do that.

ON THE OTHER HAND...

If a red-haired teacher in a funny dress shows up at your school — start packing!